JUMBO COLORING & ACTIVITY BOOK

BENDON™

HASBRO and its logo, MY LITTLE PONY and all related characters
are trademarks of Hasbro and are used with permission.
© 2011 Hasbro.
All Rights Reserved.

MAKE A MATCH

Look at the 3 ponies in each column. Find the ponies that match and draw a line connecting the two.

pony pals

WHO IS WHO?

Draw a line from each pony's cutie mark
to her correct name.

①

Ⓐ **PRINCESS CELESTIA**

②

Ⓑ **RAINBOW DASH**

③

Ⓒ **FLUTTERSHY**

COLOR BY NUMBER

Use the key below
to color the picture.

1. blue 2. red 3. pink
4. yellow 5. green 6. orange

PONY MAZE

Help Princess Celestia fly to the sun and the moon.

Find the star. ☆ Color it yellow.
Find the heart. ♡ Color it pink.
Find the diamond. ◊ Color it blue.

PONY MAZE

Help Rainbow Dash fly to her
friend Twilight Sparkle.

start

finish

FUN FiLL-iNS

Fill in the missing letters to reveal each word below.

HINT: Applejack lives there:

S_EET AP_L_

_CRES

FLUTTERSHY

HOW MANY?

Count the items below and
place your answer on the line.

_____ BUTTERFLIES.

TWiN PONiES!

Can you find the two ponies that are exactly the same?

1.

2.

3.

4.

Answer: 2 and 3 are the same.

MAKE A MATCH

Look at the 3 ponies in each column. Find the ponies that match and draw a line connecting the two.

LET'S DRAW!

Use the grid
to help you draw
a star.

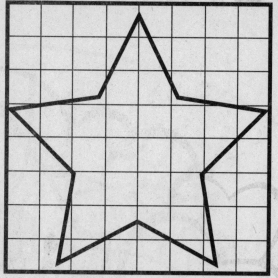

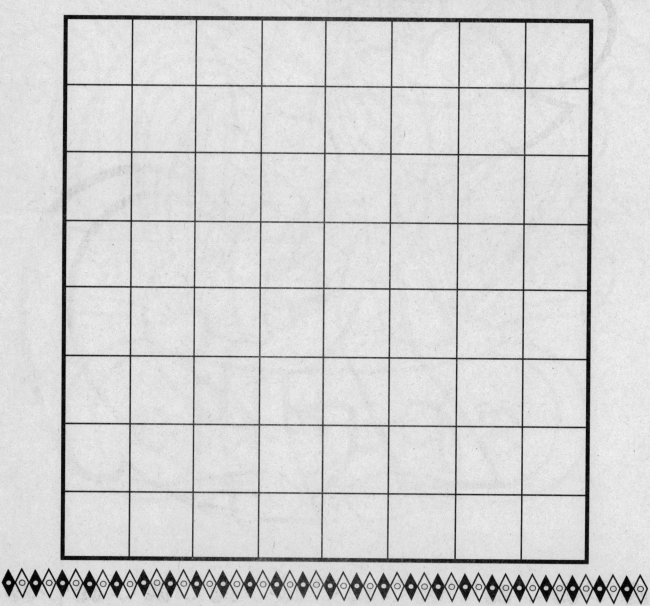

WHO IS WHO?

Draw a line from each pony's cutie mark
to her correct name.

①

Ⓐ **RARITY**

②

Ⓑ **APPLEJACK**

③

Ⓒ **TWILIGHT SPARKLE**

LET'S DRAW!

A trail of butterflies follows Fluttershy everywhere she goes. Draw some butterflies.

How 'bout them APPLES?

COLOR BY NUMBER

Use the key below
to color the picture.

1. blue 2. green 3. red
4. yellow 5. pink

PONY MAZE

Follow the path of flowers to help the
bunnies find their way to Fluttershy.

HOW MANY?

Count the items below and place your answer on the line.

_____ HEARTS.

MAKE A MATCH

Look at the 3 ponies in each column. Find the ponies that match and draw a line connecting the two.

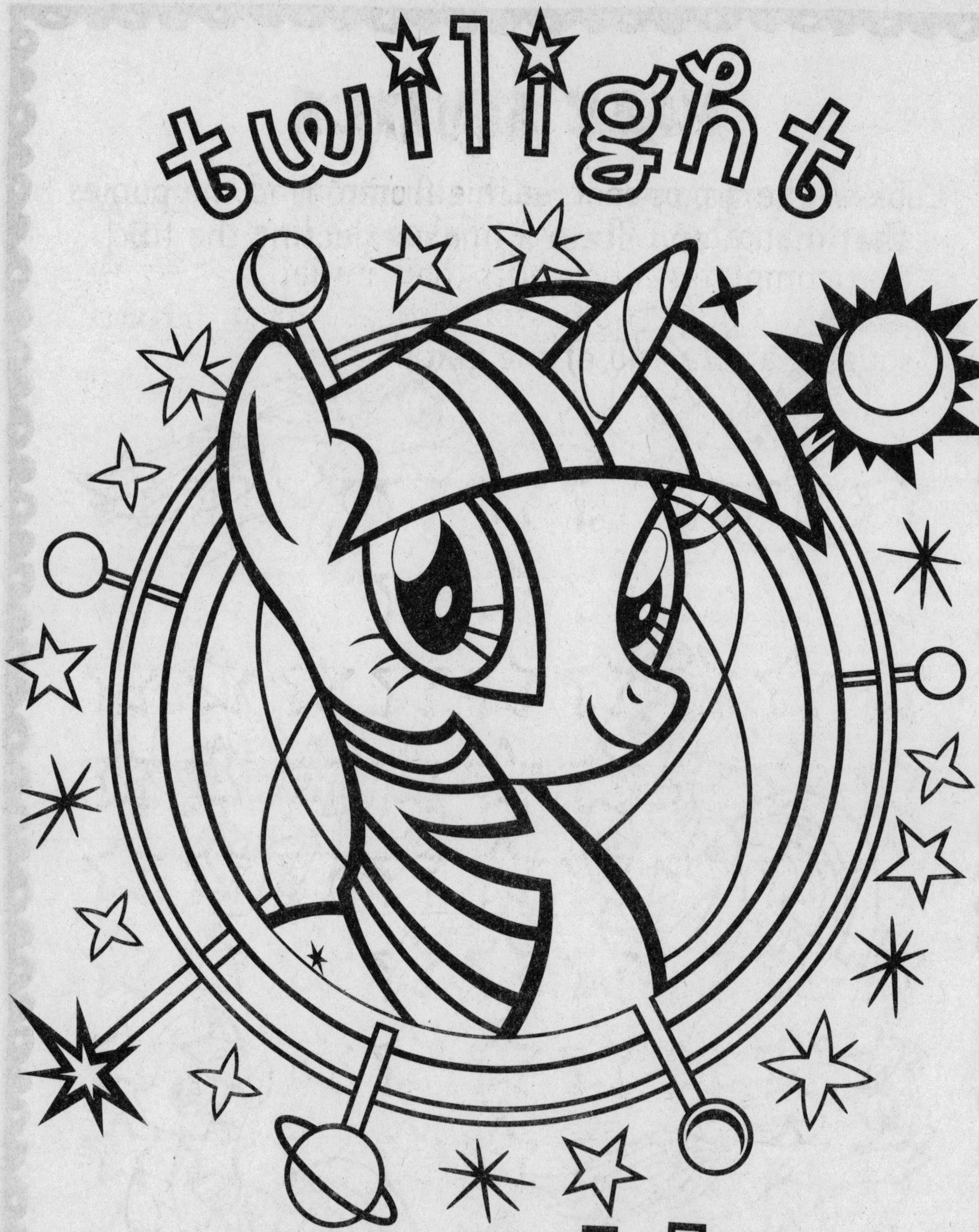
twilight
sparkle

PONY SQUARES

Taking turns, connect a line from one star to another. Whoever makes the line that completes a box puts their initial inside the box. The person with the most squares at the end of the game wins!

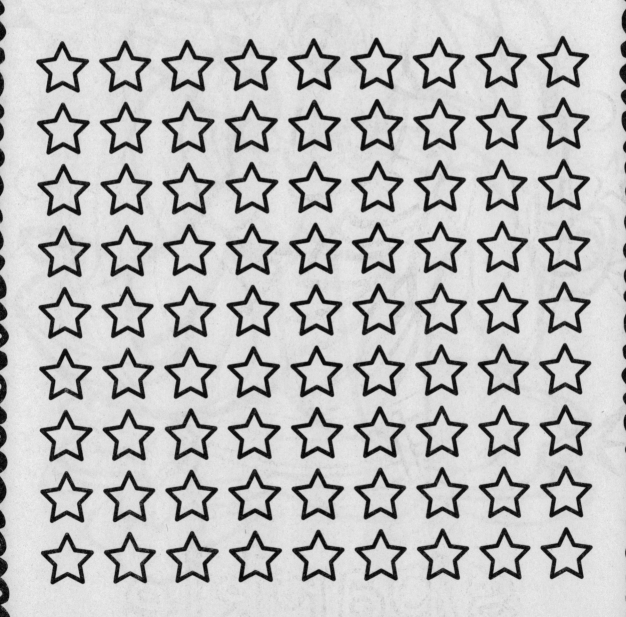

TWiN PONiES!

Can you find the two ponies that are exactly the same?

1.

2.

3.

4.

Answer: 1 and 4 are the same.

MY LITTLE PONY MIX-UP

Unscramble the words below.

iSNG

_____

UBTTERLFies

_____

NGETLE

_____

CONNECT THE DOTS

Connect the dots by alphabetical order.

FUN FiLL-iNS

Fill in the missing letters to reveal each word below.

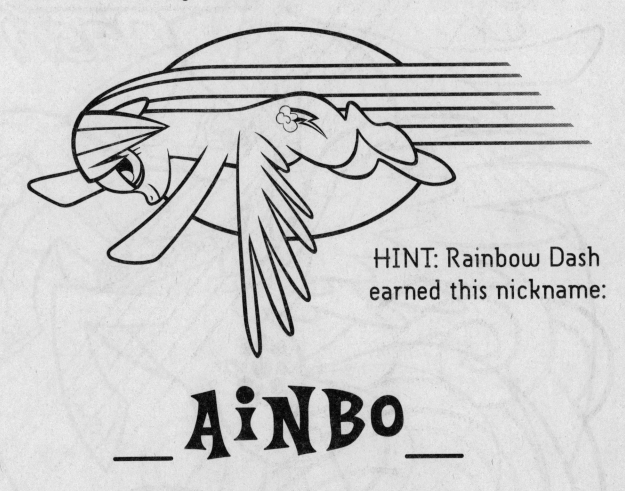

HINT: Rainbow Dash
earned this nickname:

_ AiNBO _ _

_ RASH

LET'S DRAW!

Princess Celestia is the ruler of Equestria. Draw a sun and moon.

FLUTTERSHY

CONNECT THE DOTS

Connect the dots by alphabetical order.

MY LiTTLE PONY MiX-UP

Unscramble the words below.

EBAUYT

_____

PSARLKE

_____

OBUTIQEU

_____

MAKE A MATCH

Look at the 3 ponies in each column. Find the ponies that match and draw a line connecting the two.

LET'S DRAW!

Use the grid
to help you draw a
diamond ring.

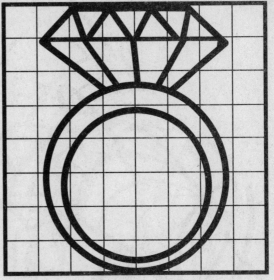

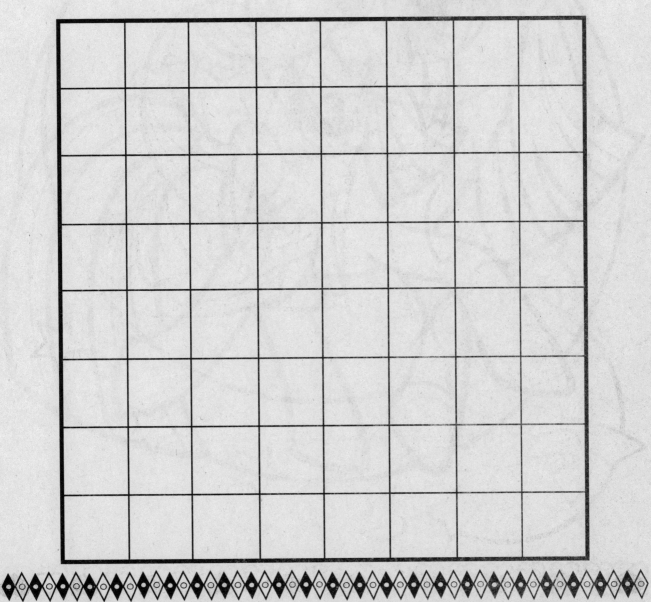

PONY MAZE

Help Spike the Dragon follow the path
of stars to Twilight Sparkle.

pony
pals

HOW MANY?

Count the items below and place your answer on the line.

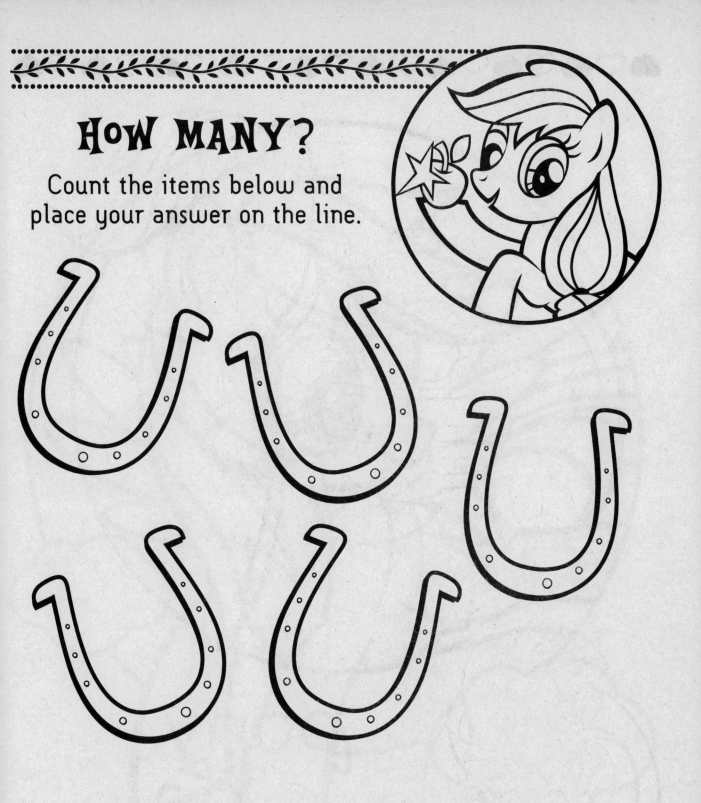

_____ HORSESHOES.

LET'S DRAW!

Rainbow Dash loves to fly!
Draw some rainbows.

MAKE A MATCH

Look at the 3 ponies in each column. Find the ponies that match and draw a line connecting the two.